MW00650616

CRISPIN: THE CROSS OF LEAD

by
Avi

Student Packet

Written by
Judith L. Martin

Edited by
Monica L. Odle

Contains masters for: 3 Prereading Activities
1 Study Guide
9 Vocabulary Activities
8 Literary Analysis Activities
1 Writing Activity
2 Comprehension Quizzes
1 Novel Test
PLUS   Detailed Answer Key

Note

The first edition, hardcover version of this book, published by Hyperion books, ©2002, was used to prpare this guide. Page references may vary in other editions.

Please note: Parts of this novel deal with sensitive, mature issues. Please assess the appropriateness of this book for the age level and maturity of your students prior to reading and discussing it with them.

ISBN 1-58130-805-1
Copyright infringement is a violation of Federal Law.

© 2003 by Novel Units, Inc., Bulverde, Texas. All rights reserved. No part of this publication may be reproduced, translated, stored in a retrieval system, or transmitted in any way or by any means (electronic, mechanical, photocopying, recording, or otherwise) without prior written permission from Novel Units, Inc.

Photocopying of student worksheets by a classroom teacher at a non-profit school who has purchased this publication for his/her own class is permissible. Reproduction of any part of this publication for an entire school or for a school system, by for-profit institutions and tutoring centers, or for commercial sale is strictly prohibited.

Novel Units is a registered trademark of Novel Units, Inc. Printed in the United States of America.

To order, contact your local school supply store, or—
Novel Units, Inc.
P.O. Box 97
Bulverde, TX 78163-0097

Web site: www.educyberstor.com

Name _____

Investigating the Middle Ages

Directions: Consult books, the Internet, and other references to investigate the Middle Ages, specifically A.D. 1300–1400. Find information to add to the attribute web. Share your information with another student and compare notes.

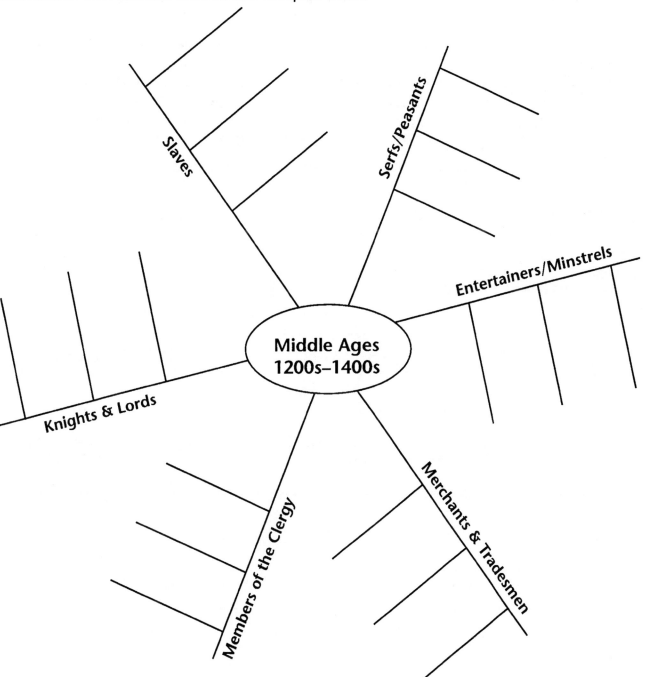

Special Note: Peasants, serfs, and slaves made up over 90% of the population in the Middle Ages.

All rights reserved

Medieval Life

1. Look at a map of Europe and find the following: England, Scotland, France, Belgium, Italy, Spain, and the Holy Lands (near Israel/Palestine). These countries are mentioned in the novel.

2. Look at a map of England and find the following cities, which are all mentioned in the novel: Canterbury, York, Winchester, and London. The story is centered around three towns and villages that are not on the map. They are Stromford, Lodgecot, and Great Wexly. As you read the book, refer to the map and predict where you think these places might be located in England, based on the main character's descriptions. Also find Gascony (SW France) and Brittany, which are mentioned in the book.

3. Research the famous people from this era mentioned in the book. Write a sentence telling why each was famous.

   a. King Edward III: _____

   _____

   b. Prince Edward, the Black Prince: _____

   _____

   c. John Ball: _____

   _____

4. The Plague: Research this epidemic, what caused it, when it happened, and how many people died. Record your findings below.

   _____

   _____

   _____

   _____

   _____

   _____

All rights reserved

Name _____

What Do You Know and Feel About...?

Directions: Think about each idea listed below. Freewrite about each for at least five minutes. Use extra paper if you need it. Be prepared to discuss your thoughts with your classmates.

1. courage

2. survival

3. freedom

4. self-confidence

5. self-reliance

6. tyranny

All rights reserved

Name _____

Directions: Write a brief answer to each study guide question as you read the novel at home or in class. Use the questions to guide your reading and to prepare for class discussion.

Chapter 1, pp. 1–5
1. What was Asta's son's mother like before she died?
2. Where is Asta's son's mother buried?
3. What does John Aycliffe demand of Asta's son?
4. What is Aycliffe's job?
5. How would you describe Aycliffe?
6. Where does Asta's son go after burying his mother?

Chapter 2, pp. 5–10
1. Why is Asta's son's head throbbing?
2. What does Asta's son see and hear in the forest?
3. What does Aycliffe do when he sees Asta's son?
4. Why does Asta's son think God is punishing him for his sins?

Chapter 3, pp. 10–13
1. Where does Asta's son live, and when was he born?
2. Where is Asta's son's father?
3. How do the other children react to Asta's son?
4. Who is Furnival?
5. What did Asta and her son do for a living?
6. What did they eat?
7. How much money did they make?

Chapter 4, pp. 13–19
1. What does Asta's son decide is his best course of action?
2. What is a *cottar*?
3. What purpose do the boundary crosses serve?
4. What does Asta's son see when he emerges from the forest?

All rights reserved

5. Why do they tear down the cottage?

6. What is north of the village?

7. What crops are grown near the village?

Chapters 5–7, pp. 20–26

1. Why is the church bell rung?

2. Who comes to the church?

3. What does Asta's son do after he hears the church bell again?

4. Why do several village men go to the manor house?

5. What is a *glaive*?

6. Where does Asta's son hide in the forest?

7. What is Asta's son accused of doing?

8. Why do Matthew and Luke talk in low voices?

Chapter 8, pp. 27–36

1. Why is St. Giles so important to Asta's son?

2. Who is the gentleman stranger?

3. What is a *wolf's head*?

4. What does Asta's son learn about himself?

5. Where does the priest tell Crispin to flee?

6. Where does the priest tell Crispin to meet him the next night?

7. What does Crispin learn about his mother?

8. Why can't Crispin make out what is written on the lead cross?

Chapters 9–13, pp. 37–54

1. What does Crispin imagine about his father?

2. Who meets Crispin outside the church?

3. What is the reward for killing Crispin?

4. What does Goodwife Peregrine give Crispin?

5. How many men are at the mill?

6. What cracks above Crispin's head?

All rights reserved

7. What does Crispin eat in the forest?

8. Why is Crispin reassured by the bailiff heading back to the village?

Chapters 14–15, pp. 54–60

1. What does Crispin find at the crossroads?

2. Which direction does Crispin travel?

3. What does Crispin eat on his third day of travels?

4. What is unusual about the village Crispin comes upon?

5. What does Crispin realize happened to the people?

6. What does Crispin hear as he is leaves the village?

Chapter 16, pp. 60–66

1. What does Crispin find in the church?

2. What does Crispin hope is in the man's sack?

3. What does the man ask Crispin?

4. What is the man's motto? What do you think it means?

5. What is *tyranny*?

6. What happens when Crispin reaches for the bread?

Chapters 17–19, pp. 66–80

1. What does Crispin tell the man when he asks where Crispin is going?

2. Why doesn't Crispin run from the man?

3. What does the man threaten to do if Crispin will not become his servant?

4. What crime did the hanged man at the crossroads commit?

5. What does the man pull from his sack?

6. Why is Crispin hesitant to tell the man his name?

7. What are Crispin's skills?

8. What is the man's real name and nickname?

9. Where is Bear going?

All rights reserved

Chapters 20–23, pp. 80–95
1. What does Crispin call his new master?
2. Why are there no people about?
3. How many people live in London? Why does this surprise Crispin?
4. What did Bear do when he was in York?
5. Why did he run off with a group of mummers?
6. What does Bear teach Crispin to do?
7. What does Bear teasingly call Crispin?
8. What do they eat?
9. What does Crispin learn about Lord Furnival's home?
10. How did Bear escape the Plague?

Chapters 24–27, pp. 95–114
1. What does Bear give Crispin the freedom to choose?
2. What does Crispin do that Bear thinks is useless?
3. What vexes Crispin the most?
4. Why does Crispin want to stay with Bear?
5. What does Crispin see in the stream?
6. What does Bear do with his dagger?
7. What does Bear do when he arrives in a village?
8. Why does Crispin feel he cannot learn music?
9. What can't Crispin feel?
10. What is a *recorder*?
11. What amazes Crispin when he plays the recorder?
12. Where do Bear and Crispin first plan to perform?
13. How many men do they see on the road at the bridge?
14. What skills does Crispin want to learn?

All rights reserved

Chapters 28–32, pp. 114–138

1. How does Bear snare birds?

2. What does Crispin make Bear promise?

3. What does Bear tell Crispin to do if there is any trouble?

4. How is Lodgecot like Stromford?

5. What do the children do as Crispin and Bear enter the village?

6. What does the priest want Bear to sing?

7. What is a *mazer*?

8. What do Bear and Crispin receive for their music and juggling?

9. What is the name of the courier that brings news to the priest?

10. Why is Crispin worried about the one-eyed youth?

11. What does "honest pay for honest work" mean?

12. What new skills does Bear teach Crispin?

Chapters 33–34, pp. 139–150

1. What type of people does Crispin see going to Great Wexly?

2. Why do people move aside and stare when Bear walks by them?

3. Why does the city have walls surrounding it?

4. What is a *portcullis*?

5. What do Crispin and Bear do when they get to the gate?

6. What are people doing inside the city walls?

7. What makes Crispin want to swoon?

8. What types of animals are in the city?

9. What do the wooden images hanging on buildings represent?

10. Where do Bear and Crispin go to conduct their affairs?

Chapters 35–37, pp. 150–163

1. What is the Green Man tavern like?

2. What important person has died? When?

3. Why is Crispin slightly jealous?

4. Why does Crispin put his hand on the wall of their room?

All rights reserved

5. What does Bear tell Crispin to do before Bear leaves?

6. What does Crispin purchase for a penny?

7. What does Crispin find exciting while wandering in the city?

8. Who does Crispin see on the black horse?

9. What do the bands of black represent?

Chapters 38–41, pp. 164–185

1. What does Crispin see in the square of the city opposite the church?

2. What is for sale in the booths and stalls?

3. What is a *vestibule*?

4. What does Crispin see in the cathedral?

5. What does Crispin use to defend himself against the two men?

6. Why can't Crispin follow the walls of the city?

7. Why do the soldiers close the gates?

8. What does Crispin do when Bear finds him?

9. Who comes to the inn to see Bear?

10. Who is the king of England? Who is his son?

Chapters 42–48, pp. 185–214

1. What day is being celebrated?

2. Who is in the Green Man tavern?

3. How much does the bread and wine at the tavern cost?

4. What does Widow Daventry assign Crispin to do in the kitchen?

5. What does Bear tell Crispin to do while Crispin stays in their room?

6. About what does Crispin want to warn Bear?

7. Where does Bear go?

8. How many men are in the meeting?

9. Where is Bear taken?

10. What does Crispin do in his room when he hears a commotion?

11. What happens to the Green Man tavern?

12. What does Widow Daventry tell Crispin to do?

All rights reserved

Chapters 49–55, pp. 214–239

1. What is written on the cross of lead?
2. Why didn't Bear tell Crispin what the cross said?
3. Why does Widow Daventry say Crispin's noble blood is poison?
4. Who is Crispin's grandfather?
5. Why does Crispin consider Bear more of a father than his real father?
6. Where does Crispin think about going when he flees the city?
7. Who leads Crispin from the Green Man tavern?
8. Who is at the White Stag tavern?
9. What does John Ball say about helping Crispin free Bear?
10. Why doesn't Crispin try to sneak into the palace on the ground level?
11. What does Crispin take from a rack in the palace?
12. What is on the altar in the palace chapel?

Chapters 56–58, pp. 240–262

1. What does Crispin have that John Aycliffe wants?
2. What does Crispin do with the dagger?
3. Where is Bear in the castle?
4. How does Bear react when the soldiers try to help him up?
5. What type of clothing do the soldiers give Bear?
6. What time is it when Crispin and Bear leave the castle?
7. What does Crispin remember to retrieve as he leaves the castle?
8. What does Crispin slip to Bear as they walk to the gates?
9. Why does Crispin leave the lead cross on Aycliffe's chest?
10. Why is Crispin's heart more full of joy than ever before?

All rights reserved

shroud (1)	pauper (2)	steward (2)	astride (2)
deigned (3)	transgression (3)	poaching (3)	forfeit (3)
manor (4)	tunic (4)	bracken (5)	cloying (5)
welt (6)	murk (6)	minions (6)	parchment (7)
affixed (7)	transfixed (8)	avail (8)	engulfed (10)

Directions: Replace each italicized phrase or word with one word from the vocabulary list.

1. The researcher found a scroll made of *animal skin prepared for writing* in the library's archives.

2. *With a leg on each side of* her horse, she rode away.

3. The *administrator* oversees the properties and the finances of the group.

4. He was punished for his *violation of the law*.

5. I was *motionless* as I viewed the beautiful sunset and the mountains.

6. After she fell on the ground, a huge *bump* appeared on her knee.

7. *Trespassing on someone's land to hunt* is punishable by law.

8. The swirling waters soon *overwhelmed* us.

9. She *attached* the stamp to the letter before mailing it.

10. On our history field trip, we saw a model of a medieval lord's *residence*.

All rights reserved

jibes (11)	embedded (11)	villeins (12)	serfs (12)
mercenary (12)	farthing (12)	tolling (13)	untoward (14)
cottar (14)	reeve (15)	wattle (15)	ford (17)
trestle (17)	run (18)	daub (18)	commons (18)
fallow (18)	crofts (19)		

Persons, Places, Things

Directions: Select words from the list above that belong in the following categories.

Persons	Places	Things That Can Be Held

All rights reserved

Name _____

sowing (20)	pealing (20)	canonical (20)	glaives (22)
hue and cry (22)	archer (23)	leagues (24)	moot (25)
alb (27)	wizened (27)	tonsured (27)	tallow (28)
lime (28)	font (28)	genuflected (29)	wolf's head (31)

Directions: Choose 15 vocabulary words from the list above. Write the words on the numbered lines below.

1. _____   2. _____

3. _____   4. _____

5. _____   6. _____

7. _____   8. _____

9. _____   10. _____

11. _____   12. _____

13. _____   14. _____

15. _____

On a separate sheet of paper, use each of the following sets of words in an original sentence. Your sentences should show that you know the meanings of the vocabulary words as they are used in the story.

Sentence 1: words 8 and 4
Sentence 2: words 9 and 3
Sentence 3: words 1 and 10
Sentence 4: words 11 and 7
Sentence 5: words 15 and 13
Sentence 6: words 3 and 6
Sentence 7: words 12 and 4
Sentence 8: words 14 and 9
Sentence 9: words 5 and 2
Sentence 10: words 7 and 6

All rights reserved

crone (39)	foreboding (40)	rasping (40)	shillings (41)
disquiet (42)	proper (43)	millrace (46)	tumult (46)
albeit (48)	rod (49)	lanced (50)	dire (52)
lurching (55)	distended (55)	pillaged (56)	dell (57)
hamlet (57)	trepidation (58)	pestilence (59)	blight (59)

Directions: Write each vocabulary word on a piece of paper (one word per piece). Using the circle below, make a spinner. Now play the following game with a classmate. (It is a good idea to have a dictionary and thesaurus handy.) Place the papers in a small container. The first player draws a word from the container. The player then spins the spinner and follows the direction where the pointer lands. For example, if the player draws the word "crone" and lands on "define," the player must define the word crone. If the player's partner accepts the answer as correct, the first player scores one point and play passes to the second player. If the player's partner challenges the answer, the first player uses a dictionary or thesaurus to prove the answer is correct. If the player can prove the answer is correct, the player earns two points. If the player cannot prove the answer is correct, the opposing player earns two points. Play continues until all the words have been used. The player with the most points wins.

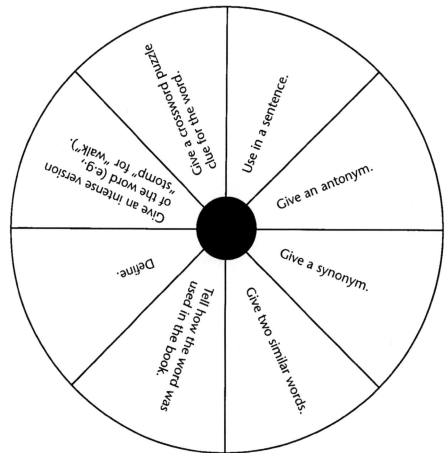

All rights reserved

ruddy (61)	bollock (62)	rents (64)	cur (64)
doddering (64)	parliaments (65)	venison (65)	sweetmeats (65)
prudence (65)	belied (66)	mockingly (67)	putrid (69)
screed (70)	pate (74)	surname (76)	henceforward (77)
wend (77)	revels (77)	guildhalls (77)	

Directions: Read each word below. The first letter of a related vocabulary word appears after each word. The related word may be either a synonym or an antonym. Write the related vocabulary word on the line. Look at each word pair. If the words are synonyms, circle them.

1. rosy—r _____

2. candies—s _____

3. dagger—b _____

4. horrible—p _____

5. quick-witted—d _____

6. bottom—p _____

7. family name—s _____

8. holes—r _____

9. sincerely—m _____

10. pedigreed dog—c _____

All rights reserved

Name _____

punctilious (83)	willy-nilly (83)	acolyte (83)	mummers (84)
beguiled (84)	faltered (85)	jeopardy (89)	stoke (90)
agape (90)	abated (90)	mirth (97)	livery (97)
heretic (100)	sham (106)	aloft (109)	spinney (111)
summit (111)	bade (112)	emblazoned (112)	paled (113)

Directions: Write each vocabulary word in the correct column below.

Noun	Verb	Adjective or Adverb
♣	✿	▲
❖	■	✖
✳	♣	♥
♦	✾	✿
✿	▲	✳
▲	♦	✾
■	❖	♦
✾	✖	♣
♥	✳	■
✖	♥	❖

Find sets of words with the same symbols. For example, the three words written beside the ▲ form a set. On a separate sheet of paper, write a sentence that includes each set of words. (Some symbols may only have one or two matches.)

All rights reserved

subdued (118)	mollify (120)	wry (122)	snuffling (124)
penance (125)	beseech (125)	mazer (126)	gambols (127)
dexterity (127)	malevolence (128)	lest (129)	courier (130)
enraptured (133)	apprentice (138)	pilgrim (139)	tinkers (141)
press (143)	portcullis (144)	gauntlet (145)	timorous (145)
palpable (146)	din (146)	portentous (147)	cacophony (147)
swill (147)	solars (149)		

Directions: Select ten vocabulary words from above. Create a crossword puzzle answer key by filling in the grid below. Be sure to number the squares for each word. Blacken any spaces not used by the letters. Then, write clues to the crossword puzzle. Number the clues to match the numbers in the squares. The teacher will give each student a blank grid. Make a blank copy of your crossword puzzle for other students to answer. Exchange your clues with someone else and solve the blank puzzle s/he gives you. Check the completed puzzles with the answer keys.

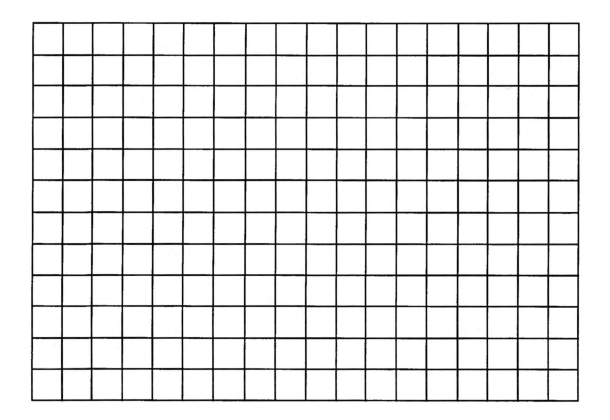

All rights reserved

Name _____

rushes (151)	kirtle (151)	pattens (151)	escapades (152)
slake (155)	furtively (156)	placating (158)	aggrieved (158)
privies (160)	buffeting (160)	disconcerted (161)	palfrey (162)
doffing (163)	personage (163)	tracery (165)	vestibule (167)
pelting (169)	nimbly (170)	ebb (173)	resumption (173)
serpentine (174)	laggards (175)	fervor (177)	vulnerable (184)

Teacher Directions:

- Photocopy and cut out the following pages.
- Give one card to each student or pair of students in the class.
- The student who has the card reading, "rushes—Who has a word that means to quench?" begins by reading his or her card aloud. The first card is starred.
- The student who has the card reading, "slake—Who has a word that means to act on the sly?" reads his or her card aloud next.
- Play continues in this manner until all cards have been read.

☆ **rushes**	**slake**
Who has a word that means to quench?	Who has a word that means to act on the sly?

furtively	**fervor**
Who has a word that means intense emotion?	Who has a word that means susceptible to attack?

vulnerable	**ebb**
Who has a word that means to decline?	Who has a word that means the opposite of ending something?

All rights reserved

resumption Who has a word that describes the act of tipping your hat?	**doffing** Who has a word that means a woman's saddled horse?
palfrey Who has a word that means frustrated or confused?	**disconcerted** Who has a word that describes something you would see in church architecture?
tracery Who has a word that means stragglers?	**laggards** Who has a word that means moving at a vigorous pace?
pelting Who has a word that describes movement similar to that of a snake?	**serpentine** Who has a word that describes a man or woman of distinction?
personage Who has a word that means sandals or wooden shoes?	**pattens** Who has a word that means grass-like marsh plants?

All rights reserved

peal (185)	leeks (190)	caterwauling (194)	broadswords (201)
chain mail (202)	protruded (207)	warrant (218)	fragmentary (221)
scabrous (225)	warren (227)	cowls (228)	succumb (229)
breach (233)	sconces (236)	spellbound (238)	disdain (240)
quaver (241)	summoning (244)	vaulted (247)	fore (247)
soot-blackened (248)	skittered (259)	impaled (260)	dub (261)
cantered (262)	unfettered (262)		

Directions: Choose five vocabulary words. Draw a picture representing each vocabulary word. Then write a meaningful paragraph using each of your chosen vocabulary words.

All rights reserved

© Novel Units, Inc.

Directions: Complete the story map as you read the novel. The solution should be added to the last box. Indicate the chapter numbers for the main events.

Story Map

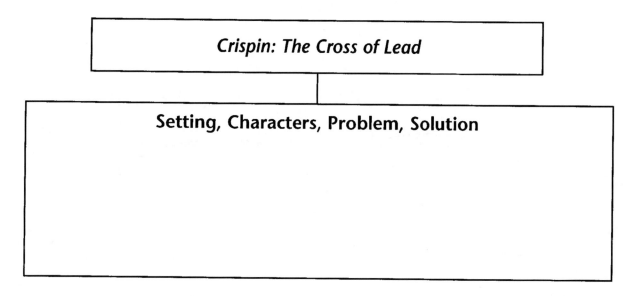

Crispin: The Cross of Lead

Setting, Characters, Problem, Solution

Series of Events

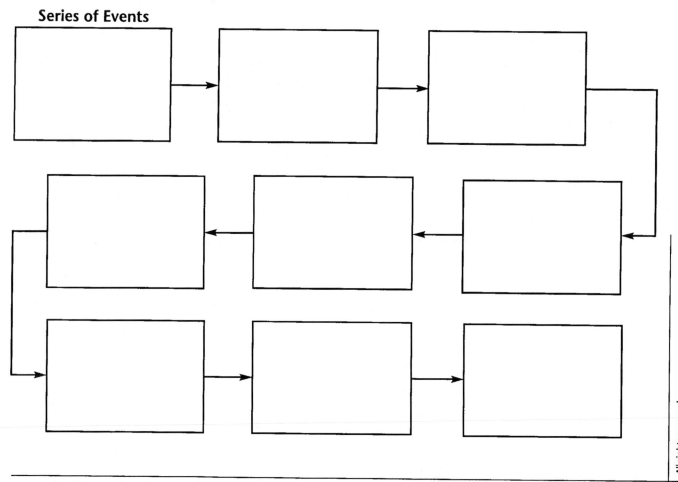

All rights reserved

Directions: Compare and contrast Crispin and Bear as they are portrayed throughout the story.

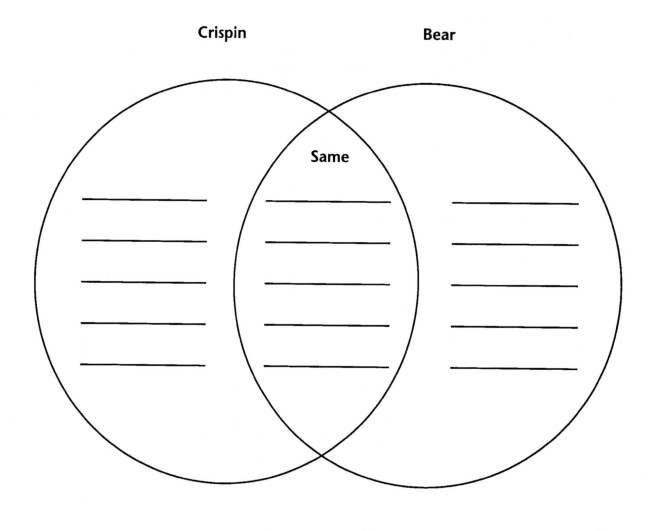

Crispin   **Bear**

Same

All rights reserved

Name _____

Character Chart

Directions: In the boxes across from each of the feelings, describe an incident or time in the book when each character experienced that feeling. You may use "not applicable" if you cannot find an example. Think of one feeling to add to the last row.

	Crispin	Bear	Aycliffe
Frustration			
Anger			
Fear			
Humiliation			
Relief			

All rights reserved

Foreshadowing Chart

Foreshadowing is the literary technique of giving clues to coming events in a story.

Directions: Think about *Crispin: The Cross of Lead.* What examples of foreshadowing do you recall from the story? If necessary, skim through the chapters to find examples of foreshadowing. List at least four examples below. Explain what clues are given, then list the coming event that is suggested.

Foreshadowing	Page #	Clues	Coming Event

All rights reserved

Name _____

Metaphors and Similes

A **metaphor** is a comparison between two unlike objects. For example, "he was a human tree." A **simile** is a comparison between two unlike objects that uses the words *like* or *as*. For example, "the color of her eyes was like the cloudless sky."

Directions: Complete the chart below by listing metaphors and similes from the novel, as well as the page numbers on which they are found. Identify metaphors with an "M" and similes with an "S." Translate the comparisons in your own words, and then list the objects being compared.

Metaphors/Similes	Ideas/Objects Being Compared
1. Translation:	
2. Translation:	
3. Translation:	

All rights reserved

Name _____

Words of Wisdom

Directions: Find examples of advice given to Crispin throughout the novel. Indicate who is giving the advice and explain what the advice means. Note the page number and tell if you agree or disagree with the advice. Use your own paper to continue the list.

Advice	Explanation	Advisor	Page	Agree or Disagree
In the midst of life comes death and in the midst of death comes life.	*Life is constantly changing and being renewed. Don't despair, have hope.*	*Father Quinel*	*1*	*A*

All rights reserved

Name _____

Thematic Analysis

Directions: Choose a theme from the book to be the focus of your word web. Complete the web and then answer the question in each starred box.

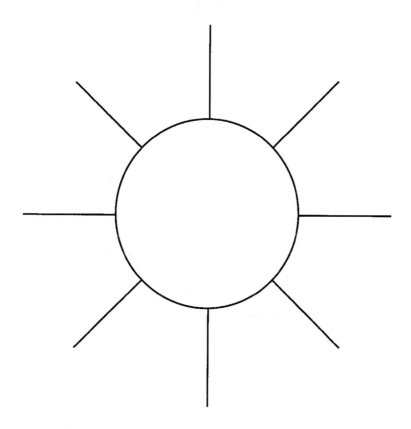

 What is the author's main message?

 What did you learn from the book?

All rights reserved

Find Out More

Directions: Select one of the following topics. Research the topic by using books, the Internet, and other data sources. Write a one-page article on your topic. Combine the articles to prepare a booklet or presentation entitled "Interesting Facts about the Middle Ages."

1. The Plague

2. Medieval social order

3. Life in a medieval village

4. Life in a medieval city

5. Role of the church in the Middle Ages

6. Guilds

7. Trade fairs and markets

8. Weapons

9. Illuminated manuscripts and calligraphy

10. Entertainment in the Middle Ages

All rights reserved

Name _____

Conflict

The **conflict** of a story is the struggle between two people or two forces. There are three main types of conflict: person against person, person against nature or society, and person against himself/herself.

Directions: The characters in *Crispin: The Cross of Lead* experience some conflicts in the story. In the chart below, list the names of three major characters. In the space provided, list a conflict each character experiences. Then explain how each conflict is resolved in the story.

Character:

Conflict	Resolution

Character:

Conflict	Resolution

Character:

Conflict	Resolution

All rights reserved

A. True/False: Mark each statement as either True (T) or False (F).

____ 1. Crispin is a good hunter and trapper.

____ 2. The one-eyed youth was delighted with Bear and Crispin's entertainment.

____ 3. Goodwife Peregrine gives Crispin three seeds, bread, and a cross.

____ 4. Bear used to be a mummer.

____ 5. The courier is Richard du Brey.

____ 6. Crispin is charged with poaching.

____ 7. Crispin earns a shilling a day working in the fields.

____ 8. Crispin's mother, Asta, was illiterate.

____ 9. Lady Furnival is related to John Aycliffe.

____ 10. Crispin's birthday is on St. Giles Day.

____ 11. The cross of lead has magical powers.

____ 12. Crispin can swim.

____ 13. Goodwife Peregrine is the oldest person in the village.

____ 14. Bear keeps Crispin's cross.

____ 15. The reward for Crispin is 10 shillings.

B. Cause/Effect: After each cause, list at least one effect.

16. The Plague:

17. Wolf's head:

18. Bear's juggling:

19. Crispin's image seen in the stream:

20. Poaching:

All rights reserved

Name _____

Short Answer: Write a brief (one- to two-sentence) answer for each question.

1. What time of the year does the story take place?

2. Why does Bear go to the Green Man tavern?

3. What do the black bands worn by the soldiers and others signify?

4. How would you describe the city?

5. Who is John Ball?

6. Why does Crispin keep slipping out of the tavern or his room?

7. How would you describe the palace in Great Wexly?

8. How does Crispin gain entrance into the palace?

9. What does Crispin give up to gain Bear's freedom?

10. What does John Ball mean by "freedom"?

All rights reserved

A. Multiple Choice

____ 1. Crispin is accused of
    a. killing his mother
    b. holding back grain from the manor
    c. stealing money from the manor
    d. poaching a stag

____ 2. Crispin's relationship with Aycliffe can be described by all of the following EXCEPT
    a. adversarial
    b. tense
    c. fearful
    d. congenial

____ 3. The village of Stromford is
    a. large
    b. bustling
    c. small
    d. commercial

____ 4. Bear teaches Crispin how to
    a. poach
    b. play the recorder
    c. read
    d. pray

____ 5. Lord Furnival was all of the following EXCEPT
    a. young
    b. authoritative
    c. rich
    d. married

____ 6. Bear had been all of the following EXCEPT a
    a. mummer
    b. bailiff
    c. monk
    d. juggler

____ 7. Aycliffe is all of the following EXCEPT
    a. benevolent
    b. cruel
    c. demanding
    d. hateful

All rights reserved

____ 8. The bells of the church tell the people all of the following EXCEPT
   a. the call to prayers
   b. the nobleman is in his palace
   c. the time of day
   d. the call for alarm

____ 9. Widow Daventry is
   a. young
   b. petite
   c. kind
   d. lazy

____ 10. John Ball wants to do all of the following EXCEPT
   a. lead a rebellion
   b. abolish unfair taxes
   c. disband the guilds
   d. meet in the town square

B. Quotations: Match the name of each character to the correct quotation. Some names will be used more than once.

____ A. Crispin

____ B. Bear

____ C. Father Quinel

____ D. John Aycliffe

____ E. Widow Daventry

____ F. John Ball

1. "You're my master...I have no choice."

2. "...that no man, or woman either, shall be enslaved, but stand free and equal to one another."

3. "...I fear you've not come to court me."

4. "Get out of the city. It's you they want, not me."

5. "Blessed Saint Giles...let me have a soul..."

6. "A great danger to us all."

7. "I beg you to find your way to some town or city with its own liberties."

8. "If you can't laugh and smile, life is worthless."

All rights reserved

9. "I...swear that I shall allow you...to leave this city insofar as you have sworn never to return..."

10. "...even the strongest can be broken by torture."

C. Essays

1. Analytical/Critical Writing (Choose A, B, or C)

A. Compare and contrast Stromford Village with the town of Great Wexly. Write a composition (four paragraph minimum) that describes the similarities and differences between country life and city life in the Middle Ages.

B. Analyze the conditions of serfs in the Middle Ages and take a position as either a noble or a reformer such as John Ball. Describe in an essay (three paragraph minimum) your views to justify your position. State your position in such a way as to not be considered treasonous.

C. Write an essay explaining two major conflicts in the novel. Explain how each conflict arose and how it is resolved, or why it is not resolved.

2. Creative Writing (Choose A or B)

A. Write a poem or lyrics for a song (a minimum of 15 lines) about the Middle Ages. Use information from the book to get ideas for the content and see the songs sung by Bear for examples of the type of language to use.

B. Write a new ending to the novel in which Crispin chooses to claim his birthright as Lord Furnival's son. Show how this affects the story's characters and outcome.

All rights reserved

Answer Key

Activity #1: Answers will vary.

Activity #2: 1.–2. Correct locations should be verified. 3. Answers will vary but may include these ideas: King Edward III—King of England from 1327–1377; Prince Edward, the Black Prince—King Edward III's son, known for riding a black horse in battle; John Ball—socialist priest who led a revolt of peasants against their lords in 1381 4. The Plague—aka the Bubonic Plague, Black Death, the Pestilence, 1347–1349, a disease carried by fleas hosting on rats; approximately 50% of Europe's population died (25 million)

Activity #3: Answers will vary.

Study Guide

Chapter 1: 1. She was small, weak, poor, pretty, and shunned by the other villagers. 2. in the paupers' cemetery behind the church 3. to bring his ox to the manor to serve as the death tax 4. He is the steward in charge of the manor, the laws, and the peasants. 5. Answers will vary. He has a black beard, hard, sharp eyes, and frowning lips. He gives cruel punishments and is demanding. 6. deep into the forest

Chapter 2: 1. He was lost, tripped and fell, and hit his head. 2. He sees Aycliffe holding a torch and a gentleman stranger with a parchment packet. They are discussing something they describe as dangerous. 3. He yells, pulls his sword, and runs after Asta's son. 4. He made Aycliffe angry, his mother died, he did not go to church, he broke curfew, and he stole wine from the church to ease his mother's pain.

Chapter 3: 1. Stromford Village, 1363 2. He died from the Plague before Asta's son's birth. 3. They taunt him, make fun of him, and hound him. 4. Lord of Stromford Village, a soldier off at war 5. worked in the fields from dawn to dusk, fed the animals, gathered wood and brush for heat, slept, and tried to stay alive 6. barley bread, watered ale, cooked dried peas, sometimes meat 7. Asta made a penny a day, and her son made a farthing a day.

Chapter 4: 1. to return to the village and his cottage and pretend nothing happened with Aycliffe 2. a person who holds no land in his/her own right 3. They mark the limits of the village. 4. The bailiff and reeve are carrying tools toward his cottage and begin to tear it down. 5. Answers will vary. 6. the commons—land where oxen and sheep graze, archers practice, and people are punished in the public stocks or hanged on the gallows 7. barley and wheat

Chapters 5–7: 1. to announce important news 2. all the villagers, the priest, Aycliffe, and the gentleman stranger 3. prays 4. They were told to go to the manor by the steward in order to help search for Asta's son. 5. a long pole with a sharp blade attached 6. in a great oak tree thick with leaves 7. breaking into the manor house and stealing money 8. If they are overheard to disagree with the steward, they could be hanged for treason.

Chapter 8: 1. Asta's son was born on St. Giles Day, and Giles is the village's patron saint. 2. Richard du Brey, a messenger for Lord Furnival 3. an outlaw that anyone may kill 4. His mother named him Crispin when he was born but kept it secret. 5. to a town or city with its own liberties, or to an abbey 6. at Goodwife Peregrine's house 7. Asta could read and write. 8. He cannot read.

Chapters 9–13: 1. He worried his father was an outlaw or traitor or someone exiled from the church. 2. Cerdic, a village boy 3. 20 shillings (half a year's wages) 4. a leather pouch, porridge, and bread 5. eight 6. an arrow 7. acorns and bitter roots 8. Answers will vary; maybe the bailiff has given up on finding Crispin.

Chapters 14–15: 1. a dead man hung on gallows 2. "westerly" 3. only water as he cannot find any food 4. no people live there, roofs collapsed, walls fallen, carts broken, tools scattered, dirty water 5. The Great Plague killed everyone in the village. 6. a voice singing

Chapter 16: 1. a large man dressed in colorful clothes 2. food 3. where he comes from, where he's going, how he appears, and if he is hungry 4. "Let it be as it may be." Answers will vary. 5. a government where one ruler is vested with all the power 6. The man grabs his wrist.

All rights reserved

Chapters 17–19: 1. He is going to a town to save himself because he ran away after being proclaimed a wolf's head. 2. The man has hold of Crispin's wrist and later blocks the doorway with his body. 3. return him to the steward 4. He held back or "stole" a pound of wool from his master to sell for food for his sick child. 5. three stitched leather balls with which he juggles 6. Crispin is not yet comfortable with his newfound name since he was called Asta's son for 13 years. 7. He can follow ox, sow seed, gather crops, and thresh wheat and barley. 8. Orson Hrothgar, Bear 9. to Great Wexly

Chapters 20–23: 1. "Sir Bear" 2. Many people died from the Plague or pestilence. 3. 30,000–40,000; Crispin came from a village of 150 and can't imagine such a large city. 4. studied to be a priest 5. He liked the mummers' music, tricks, and laughter. 6. juggle and play the recorder 7. Saint Crispin 8. roasted rabbit and bread 9. Lord Furnival's first home is in Great Wexly, where they are going. 10. He ran north to Scotland.

Chapters 24–27: 1. The choice is to join or not join Bear to entertain in the villages. 2. Crispin holds the cross of lead and prays, and Bear says they do not have special powers. 3. the idea that every man should be master of himself 4. Crispin feels Bear will feed him, protect him, and let him survive, at least for a while. 5. He sees his reflection and realizes his hair is long, his face is dirty, bruised and tear-streaked, and his eyes are red. 6. cuts Crispin's hair 7. goes to the church or manor and applies to the priest, lord, bailiff and/or reeve to seek permission to perform 8. He is not confident in his abilities. 9. his soul 10. a pipe with holes or stops and a blowing end 11. He is amazed that he can make music and that Bear can dance. 12. at the village of Burley 13. twelve 14. nature and survival skills

Chapters 28–32: 1. He uses a few long horsetail hairs, tying the strands to make a loop. 2. to return his lead cross to him 3. run far north out of the kingdom 4. The people are dressed in similar styles, they work in the fields the same way, and the buildings are similar. 5. The children approach them with curiosity. 6. sacred music 7. a large wooden bowl 8. a few pennies and some bread 9. du Brey 10. The one-eyed youth grew angry with them when Bear teased him. 11. Crispin had worked hard and earned the money honestly. 12. how to use weapons, snare an animal, and look people in the eyes

Chapters 33–34: 1. a pilgrim, a rich person, peasants, merchants, priests, nuns, monks, officials, tradesmen, traders, tinkers, masons, carpenters, doctor, lawyer, apothecary, tax collector, soldiers 2. Bear is so large and confident that people don't want to get in his way. 3. to keep the enemies out and the citizens safe 4. a sliding grill of iron or wood fixed in a gateway so it can be closed quickly 5. Crispin plays the pipe, and Bear dances. 6. shouting, calling, arguing, laughing, and selling their wares 7. the stench in the air of rotting goods, food, dung, manure, human slop, and swill 8. pigs, chickens, geese, dogs, and rats 9. The wooden signs represent what type of businesses are in the buildings. 10. The Green Man tavern

Chapters 35–37: 1. It is a dim, smoky, smelly place with low ceilings and wooden floors covered with dirty rushes. There are trestle tables and benches and a counter with rows of wooden tankards. 2. Lord Furnival, two weeks ago 3. Widow Daventry knows more about Bear and his business than Crispin does. 4. Crispin has never been on the second floor of a building, and he is afraid it will fall down. 5. stay in the room until he returns 6. white bread 7. The twists and turns in the streets are intriguing to him, and one has to make a choice in which direction to go. 8. Lady Furnival 9. The bands signify someone has died, and the people are in mourning.

Chapters 38–41: 1. a large stone three-story building with large windows off the balconies, blue and gold flags, and stone lions' heads 2. cloth, furs, daggers, hats, gloves, baskets, boxes, boots, shoes, tools, armor, food, spices 3. a small entranceway 4. Aycliffe 5. Bear's dagger 6. The wall was not a simple circle but serpentine, like a snake. 7. It is curfew, and the city is closing for the night. 8. hugs Bear and tells him about being attacked 9. John Ball, a priest 10. King Edward and his son the Duke of Lancaster

Chapters 42–48: 1. Feast of St. John the Baptist 2. tradesmen, peasants, men in livery, some women 3. one penny each 4. watch the pies in the oven, bake the breads, add more wood to the fire 5. practice his music 6. The one-eyed youth is spying on Bear and is showing Lord Furnival's men the direction in which Bear has gone. 7. to a three-story building with a shuttered window and a sign with a boot to meet

All rights reserved

 © Novel Units, Inc.

John Ball and other men 8. seven 9. to Furnival's palace 10. hides in a secret compartment 11. The soldiers demolish it; they smash tables, split benches and the counter, break tankards, and rough up Widow Daventry. 12. stay upstairs in the secret area until curfew and then escape the city

Chapters 49–55: 1. Son of Furnival 2. to protect Crispin 3. Answers will vary. She does not respect the nobility. Also, Lady Furnival will be threatened by Crispin and will see him as an enemy rather than as a stepson. 4. probably Lord Douglas 5. Bear protects Crispin, provides for him, and teaches him skills like a father should do for a son. Lord Furnival banished Crispin and Asta to Stromford Village to live as peasants. 6. Scotland 7. a man hired by Widow Daventry 8. John Ball and four other men 9. They feel Bear has lost his way regarding their brotherhood, and the other men can't be further endangered. 10. There are two guards on the ground level. 11. a dagger 12. an image of a knight and the Virgin Mary, relic boxes, and candles

Chapters 56–58: 1. the cross of lead proclaiming Crispin is the son of Furnival 2. He knocks Aycliffe down, holds the dagger to his neck, and draws blood. 3. in a cellar 4. He rears back like a wounded beast and strikes their hands away. 5. a cloak 6. dawn 7. Bear's sack with his two-pointed hat and pennies 8. the dagger 9. Answers will vary. He took a vow to give the cross to Aycliffe so he leaves it even though Aycliffe is dying; Crispin does not want it any longer as it brings him grief. 10. He is safe, free, and has a friend.

Activity #4: 1. parchment 2. astride 3. steward 4. transgression 5. transfixed 6. welt 7. poaching 8. engulfed 9. affixed 10. manor

Activity #5: Persons—villeins, serfs, cottar, reeve; Places—ford, crofts, commons; Things That Can Be Held—farthing, wattle, daub. Sketches will vary.

Activities #6–#7: Answers will vary.

Activity #8: 1. ruddy 2. sweetmeats 3. bollock 4. putrid 5. doddering 6. pate 7. surname 8. rents 9. mockingly 10. cur; Circle #1, 2, 3, 4, 7, 8

Activity #9: Nouns—acolyte, mummers, jeopardy, mirth, livery, heretic, sham, spinney, summit; Verbs—beguiled, faltered, stoke, abated, bade, emblazoned, paled; Adjectives—punctilious; Adverbs—willy-nilly, agape, aloft

Activity #10: Answers will vary.

Activity #11: Words are in the correct order on the cards on pages 20–21 of this guide.

Activity #12: Answers will vary.

Activity #13: Answers will vary. Suggestions—*Setting:* fourteenth–century medieval England; *Characters:* Crispin—narrator and hero of story; Bear—former monk now in disguise as an entertainer (jester, singer), mentor of Crispin; John Aycliffe—steward of the manor in Stromford, brother of Lady Furnival, searching for Crispin to kill him; *Problem:* Crispin, hunted as a criminal, leaves his village and tries to save his life; *Solution:* Bear helps Crispin and teaches him to become self-reliant and free; *Events:* 1. Crispin's mother dies, and his home is torn down. 2. Crispin is accused of stealing money (Ch. 4, 7). 3. Crispin learns his name, is declared a wolf's head, and finds Father Quinel murdered (Ch. 8–12). 4. Crispin wanders and meets Bear, who makes him his servant (Ch. 15–18). 5. Crispin and Bear discuss views of life and the future; entertain in villages (Ch. 24–32) 6. They go to Great Wexly; Crispin narrowly escapes Aycliffe in cathedral (Ch. 34–39). 7. Crispin warns Bear and John Ball of soldiers, but Bear is caught (Ch. 44–46). 8. Crispin bargains with Aycliffe in the palace to free Bear (Ch. 52–56). 9. Crispin and Bear leave the city as safe and free men (Ch. 57–58).

Activity #14: Answers will vary. Suggestions—Crispin: young, serf, illiterate, meek, serious, unconfident; Bear: middle-age, large, strong, boisterous, humorous, literate, former monk, juggler, self-confident; Both: kind, caring, trustworthy, honest, smart, free, self-reliant

Activity #15: Answers will vary.

All rights reserved

Activity #16: Samples of foreshadowing from book include: "Concerned that I had been observed, I stood still and scrutinized the place where I'd seen movement" (p. 35)—foreshadows that Cerdic or others are watching him to trap him; "...I'm part of a brotherhood. It's to make things better. To bring some change" (p. 120)—foreshadows Bear's involvement in an underground political group; "...I was more than a little hesitant, knowing his business—as he had said himself—was dangerous" (p. 150)—foreshadows the risk Bear is taking and that the brotherhood meets illegally; "...Father Quinel had told me once at confession: a moment of silence in the midst of talk means Death's Angel is close at hand," (p. 155)—foreshadows someone will die; "Because...if you don't help him, things could go much the worse for you both" (p. 192)—foreshadows that Crispin will help Bear and that they are in for more trouble.

Activity #17: Answers will vary.

Activity #18: Some examples include: "Bread is never free, boy," meaning people who give you things want something in return—Bear (p. 66); "If you can't laugh and smile, life is worthless," meaning don't be so serious and lighten up so your life can be better—Bear (p. 73); "Music is the tongue of souls," meaning music lets one express one's true self—Bear (p. 77); "For mirth is the coin that brings a welcome," meaning happiness and joyfulness are better for life than sadness and sorrow—Bear (p. 97); "Lose your sorrows, and you'll find your freedom," meaning if you stop worrying you will be better able to influence your life—Bear (p. 97); "...living by answers is a form of death. It's only questions that keep you living," meaning that you have to keep alert, keep observing, and be curious to really be happy—Bear (pp. 97–98); "...a man's soul may be observed behind the eyes," meaning how someone looks at you tells you a lot about the person and his/her motives—Bear (p. 135); "The worst disguise is fear," meaning if someone can tell you are afraid, the person may take advantage of you—Bear (p. 145); "...less said, less to deny," meaning one does not have to lie if one is careful not to say too much—Bear (p. 194)

Activity #19: Answers will vary. The themes include freedom, self-reliance, self-confidence, survival, and identity.

Activities #20–#21: Answers will vary.

Comprehension Quiz #1: A. 1. F 2. F 3. T 4. T 5. T 6. F 7. F 8. F 9. T 10. T 11. F 12. F 13. T 14. F 15. F **B.** 16.–20. Answers will vary but may include: 16. many deaths, abandoned villages, orphans, shortage of workers 17. Crispin had to flee, always be afraid and alert, could be caught and killed 18. source of money and food, opportunity to travel, opportunity to talk to villagers 19. wash face with sand, cut hair 20. hanging, penalty, death

Comprehension Quiz #2: 1. June. 2. He is friends with Widow Daventry and trusts her. His room in the tavern has a secret compartment. 3. mourning because of the death of Lord Furnival 4. Answers will vary, but should include crowded, dirty, or smelly. 5. John Ball is a priest who is upset with the way serfs and peasants are treated. He wants to rebel against the nobles. 6. He is curious, excited, and worried about Bear. 7. Answers will vary, but should include plush, richly furnished, large, or well-guarded. 8. He pushes himself up between the walls of the palace and the building next door, swings over a statue, and lands on the balcony of the second floor. 9. He gives up his claim and rights as son of Lord Furnival, as well as his cross of lead. 10. Answers will vary.

Novel Test: A. 1. c 2. d 3. c 4. b 5. a 6. b 7. a 8. b 9. c 10. d **B.** 1. A (p. 98) 2. F (p. 200) 3. E (p. 152) 4. B (p. 204) 5. A (p. 110) 6. D (p. 8) 7. C (p. 32) 8. B (p. 73) 9. D (p. 245) 10. E (p. 213) **C.** Answers will vary.

All rights reserved

 © Novel Units, Inc.